P9-CEY-040

The Heart of a Nurse Leader

of a

Values-Based Leadership for Healthcare Organizations

BOB DENT & JOE TYE

The Heart of a Nurse Leader

Values-Based Leadership for Healthcare Organizations

BOB DENT & JOE TYE

DEDICATION

This book is dedicated to all the men and women
who have chosen to be nurse leaders, whether or not
they have a management title. And of course to
Karen and Sally with all our hearts.

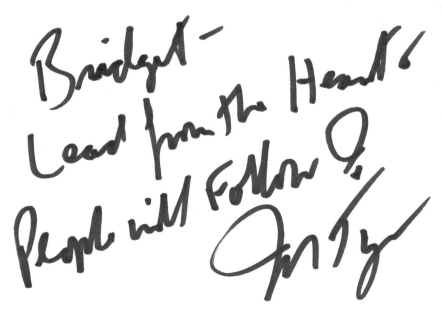

ACKNOWLEDGMENTS

In addition to the many people we acknowledged in our last book, *Building a Culture of Ownership in Healthcare*, we want to recognize how AONE puts leadership into the heart of a nurse leader, and how the DAISY Foundation puts heart into the leadership of a nurse leader.

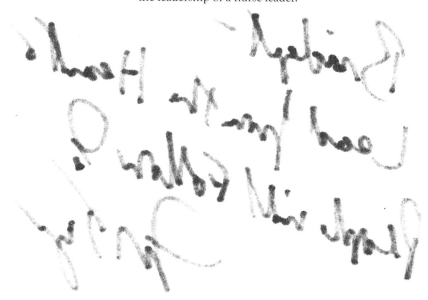

INTRODUCTION

THE TWELVE CORE
ACTION VALUES

*The goals you achieve, the contribution you make, and the person
you become will be guided by the values that guide your life.*

The Twelve Core Action Values* which form the structure of this
book, is a philosophy of values-based life and leadership. The
course features twelve values that are universal. Regardless of your
religious belief or non-belief, political opinions, ethnic background,
professional occupation or any other factor, these are your values. But
without action, even the most well-intentioned values are just that
– good intentions. Therefore, each of the twelve values rests upon
four cornerstones that help to put action into the value. The first six
values help to establish personal character strength and the second
six values help to achieve goals and make a contribution.

We have seen the life-changing and culture-transforming impact
of these values at Midland Health and at many other organizations –
and in our own lives as well. Our friend and colleague Dave Altman,

Chief Operating Officer of the world-famous Center for Creative Leadership, says that The Twelve Core Action Values are like graduate school for the seven habits. We take that one step further and say that they are like graduate school for life. The heart of a nurse leader begins with a commitment to values; from Authenticity through to Leadership, we are confident that these are your values.

One of the key insights we've gained in our work is that *organizational values* – the plaque on the wall – define operational outcomes and determine business strategies, while *personal values* shape culture and influence workplace attitudes and relationships. One of the best investments any organization can make is having a powerful and authentic statement of organizational core values, helping individual associates clarify and solidify their own personal values, and then assuring alignment between the two.

In his book *What Got You Here Won't Get You There*, Marshall Goldsmith wrote that in his many years of coaching Fortune 100 executives, one of the most important lessons he'd learned is that people will not make fundamental personal changes in their attitudes or behaviors unless those changes are guided by their personal values. Since culture does not change unless and until people change, the first step toward cultural transformation is often helping individuals crystallize and operationalize the personal values that guide those changes.

This book is meant to inspire nurse leaders in all settings and at every level to be a little bit better. For nurse leaders to create and sustain a more positive workplace environment that is void of toxic behaviors, where people can be and do their best. Nurse leaders must model the way themselves first. And remember, nurse leader is not necessarily a formal title. All nurses can lead from where they are.

* A description of the Values Coach course on The Twelve Core Action Values, is included in Appendix 1.

CONTENTS

Living Your Values

"If people could understand their core values, they would save years of doubt, confusion, and misplaced energy as they try to find direction for their lives."

Laurie Beth Jones: Jesus CEO

The first responsibility of the nurse leader is to be clear about his or her own values, and to make a concerted daily effort to assure that these values are reflected in the attitudes they bring to work, the way they treat people, their approach to dealing with conflict, the criteria they use for making decisions, and how they deal with obstacles and setbacks. The second responsibility – the one that more than any other single quality defines the heart of a nurse leader – is to help the people whom they lead do the same thing.

We have both devoted our entire careers to healthcare and we know that the people who are attracted to the healing professions intuitively have good solid values. However, we also know that most of us have not clearly defined what those values are. We do not adequately monitor how those values are reflected in our relationships and in the goals we seek to achieve, or in the entries in our calendars and in our checkbook registers.

Investing in training for personal values is a classic example of Quadrant II in Stephen Covey's well-known time management grid: Important but Not Urgent. Your people no doubt intuitively have good values – it is the heart of nursing leadership to expect them to live those values, and to help them do it. It only takes one person living their values and doing the right thing to make a difference in the people around them.

Personal Values and Organizational Commitment

"We know from our research that the people who are clearest about their [personal] vision and values are significantly more committed to their organizations than are those who are not clear about their vision and values."

James M. Kouzes and Barry A. Posner:
A Leader's Legacy

As part of orientation, every new associate of Midland Health completes a two-day course on The Twelve Core Action Values – something all current associates have already done. Inculcating The Twelve Core Action Values into the cultural fabric of the organization was the single-most important element of the cultural turnaround that we described in our book *Building a Culture of Ownership in Healthcare* (Sigma Publishing, 2017). The course is also a central component of the organization's vision that Midland will become the healthiest community in Texas. As the next step in this journey, the course is now being integrated into the cultural fabric of the Midland Independent School District.

One of the tools we use to assess values statements is the Values→Behaviors→Outcomes Continuum. Such things as quality, safety, and patient satisfaction are outcomes. Personal behaviors such as professionalism, attentiveness, and cheerfulness achieve those outcomes. And those behaviors are inspired by personal values.

Helping your associates become better people - not just as employees but as parents, as citizens, and as human beings – is the gift to your colleagues that is also an investment in your organization.

Skills Put Action into Values

People can learn the skills that are necessary to put action into their values and transform good intentions into real-world outcomes.

When we teach The Twelve Core Action Values, we are not teaching values per se. As we've mentioned, people in the healing professions intuitively have good solid values. Rather, we are teaching people *skills* that will help them more effectively live those values.

As we previously mentioned, these twelve values are universal. Every single one of us holds Authenticity (Core Action Value #1) as a personal value. Nobody aspires to be a fake, a fraud, or a phony. Yet we all struggle to achieve self-awareness, self-mastery, self-belief and self-truth – the four cornerstones of Authenticity. To become more authentic, we can learn meditation skills for introspection; we can work with a coach to learn how to better master our ego and manage our emotions; we can learn to confront negative self-talk and self-imposed barriers to achieve our potential; and we can seek meaningful feedback to help us more consistently be our best selves.

Learning to practice these skills is how you put action into your values; teaching your people to practice these skills is how you assure that those values are reflected in the culture of your organization.

Organizational Values and Personal Values

Organizational values determine your strategies while personal values shape your culture.

However they are worded, most healthcare organizations share a common set of core values that include such qualities as compassion, commitment to safety and quality, effective stewardship of resources, a respectful and progressive workplace environment, and the promise of integrity and ethical behavior. But many of the values listed in the organization's statement of values are not values per se. Compassion, stewardship and professionalism are not values, they are valued behaviors. And quality, safety, and patient satisfaction are not values, they are valued outcomes. There is nothing wrong with including behaviors and outcomes in a statement of values – they can help to determine the strategies the organization employs to achieve its goals.

Personal values like those included in The Twelve Core Action Values inspire the behaviors that achieve the desired outcomes. Organizational culture is shaped by personal values – one attitude, one behavior, one interaction at a time. We have seen this time and again: helping someone learn skills to be a better parent inevitably inspires them to be a better caregiver; helping them learn skills to achieve their personal financial goals inevitably inspires them to be a better steward of the organization's resources.

One of the best investments an organization can make in gaining employee alignment with their organizational values is to help individual people think about and act upon their personal values.

Closing the Values Gap

There is always a gap between the values that are posted on the wall and the way those values are reflected in the workplace; the challenge of leadership is to close that gap.

The words in the values plaque on the wall and on the recruiting pages of the website define your organization's best intentions. But to be real, they must also be reflected in the attitudes and behaviors of the people who do the work. Unfortunately, there is always a gap between those good intentions and actual performance.

If your organization's statement of values calls for integrity, but your workplace culture tolerates people talking about co-workers behind their backs, then there is a values gap. Gossip and rumor-mongering are dishonest, disrespectful, and a cruel disservice to the person about whom rumors are being spread.

Fortunately, it is within the power of the leader to close the values gap. In an organization where integrity is taken seriously as a value, as soon as the rumor mill starts to churn, someone will have the courage to say, "In our organization we insist upon integrity, so we do not talk about other people behind their backs." That is putting action into the value.

Changing Culture by Teaching Values

Culture does not change unless and until people change, but people will not sustain personal change unless that change is inspired by their own core values.

The culture of your organization is shaped by the collective attitudes and behaviors of the people who work there. If no one is willing to change their attitudes and their behaviors; if everyone thinks that a poor culture is someone else's fault and that enhancing that culture is someone else's responsibility, then culture will never change for the better (though it might well continue to deteriorate).

Here's what we consistently find when we conduct the validated VCI-17 Culture Assessment Survey for Values Coach client organizations. Without exception, more than 90 percent of respondents agree or strongly agree with the statements "I am personally committed to the values of this organization" and "I am personally determined to do my best work every day." But when the same question is asked of the respondent's *co-workers*, the proportion of "agree" or "strongly agree" responses diminishes sharply. It's the Lake Woebegone Effect, where everyone thinks that they are above average.

It takes courage to take off the rose-colored glasses when you look in the mirror and assess your own attitudes and behaviors. Leading with heart inspire their people to do just that.

Values, Accountability and Ownership

You can hold people accountable for adhering to the organization's statement of values, but you cannot hold them accountable for living up to their personal values – that must be inspired by a sense of ownership.

The management buzzword of the 1990's was "Empowerment," but today we hear that word much less often. "Empowerment" has been replaced by "Accountability" as the buzzword of the day. It's as if we tried the empowerment trick and it didn't work, so now we are going to crack the whip and hold people's feet to the fire (to quote two of the most frequently-cited metaphors for holding someone accountable).

Especially in healthcare, though, you cannot hold people accountable for the things that really matter. You cannot crack the whip to make people more compassionate or empathetic. Holding people's feet to the fire will not foster pride or increase loyalty. Carrots and sticks do not generate genuine enthusiasm and commitment. When you say to someone that "I'm going to hold you accountable for..." the implicit message is that you don't trust them to hold themselves accountable.

As Richard Farson and Ralph Keyes show in their book *The Innovation Paradox*, in the short-term a culture focused on accountability can achieve results, but over the long run it "encourages a culture of evasion, denial, and finger-pointing." When people are clear about, committed to, and acting upon their own personal values, they do not need to be held accountable because they take ownership for their attitudes, their behaviors, and their outcomes. You don't have to hold someone's feet to the fire if they are willing to walk across hot coals on their own.

CORE ACTION VALUES 1-6

The Foundation of Personal Character Strength

1. Authenticity

2. Integrity

3. Awareness

4. Courage

5. Perseverance

6. Faith

THE TWELVE CORE
ACTION VALUES

———————————

The goals you achieve

The contribution you make

The person you become

*Will be determined by the values
that guide your life*

Chapter One

AUTHENTICITY

CORNERSTONES

Self-Awareness

Self-Mastery

Self-Belief

Self-Truth

Do you want to be one *of* a million or one *in* a million?

AUTHENTICITY

*The greatest triumph of the human spirit
is to become the person you were meant
to be, and pursue the goals that you
were put on this earth to achieve.
The greatest tragedy is to spend your life
pretending to be someone other than your
meant-to-be best self because you
think you'll impress people and
make more money.*

How do leaders influence and inspire others to be their best selves? More than anything it is through their own example. Nobody wants to follow someone that they perceive as a fake, a fraud or a phony.

Authenticity is not a state of being nearly so much as it is a state of becoming, of striving toward the genuine human being that you are truly meant to be. One of the most stressful conditions is acting out of authenticity, pretending to be somebody you're not, or giving in to impulses that reflect poorly on the real you. It is in those situations you are most likely to regret something you have done or said, or to exclaim that you just weren't being yourself.

Management is a job description. Leadership is a life decision. Authenticity is the first step in a journey that culminates in leadership. The heart of a nurse leader begins by being authentic – being true to the calling that inspired you to enter the profession. And by helping others be authentic, the nurse leader nurtures other nurse leaders.

Self-Awareness

The one face on the face of the earth
that you are forever prohibited from
viewing directly is your own; you are only
permitted to see indirect reflections.
That is a perfect metaphor for achieving
self-awareness – it requires
indirect measures.

The nurse leader must recognize that self-awareness has both an inner and an outer dimension, and conscientiously work to cultivate both. The inner dimension is a deep appreciation of her strengths and weaknesses, sources of personal motivation, and emotional tripwires. A nurse leader pays acute attention to self-talk, knowing when to ignore it and when to talk back to it, and is deliberate about nurturing positive emotions that enhance her performance and starving negative emotions that inhibit the ability to be an effective leader.

The outer dimension is a thoughtful awareness of how attitudes, moods and actions influence the people around her. It includes an appreciation that both the power of position and the power of personality give disproportionate influence over the attitudes, moods and behaviors of the people for whom she is responsible and is very deliberate in her commitment to setting a positive example.

The nurse leader enhances inner awareness with such disciplines as meditation, prayer, introspection and journaling. Socrates said that the greatest wisdom is to know yourself. But that is much easier said than done. She enhances outer awareness by objectively observing how others react to her, and by seeking and heeding regular feedback from multiple sources.

Self-Mastery

---

*The foundation of emotional
intelligence is a commitment to mastering
your ego and managing your emotions
so that you never become your
own worst enemy.*

Malcolm Gladwell's book *The Tipping Point* described how small things can add up to make a big difference. For many of us, though, a more relevant title would be *The Tripping Point*, about how seemingly minor deficiencies in character, attitudes, behaviors, and habits can accumulate to trip you up and prevent you from achieving your personal, professional, and financial goals and, in the worst case, bring about catastrophic failure on these fronts. How that tripping point can cause you to be defeated by YOWE – Your Own Worst Enemy.

Every time you defeat your lesser self and overcome your lesser impulses, you become a stronger and better person and move closer to the achievement of your most important goals and dreams. Every time your lesser self – YOWE – defeats you, you settle for anemic dreams and goals and a little bit more of your authentic best self – the YOU that you are meant to be – dies.

What business does one have seeking to lead others who has not first learned to lead himself, Confucious asked his followers. Leading with heart begins with an act of self-mastery.

Self-Belief

---

*If you don't believe in yourself,
no one else will believe in you. If you don't
believe in your dreams, you won't inspire
others to believe in your dreams.*

At one time or another, in one way or another, we all struggle with a poor self-image and low self-esteem; we all settle for anemic dreams and goals because the voice of negative self-talk has convinced us that we're not capable of more and that we don't deserve better; and in selling ourselves short, we let down the people who depend upon us to help them achieve their goals and dreams.

The nurse leader challenges his self-limiting beliefs, self-imposed barriers and self-confining assumptions. He knows that there are occasions when this means that he must "fake it till he makes it" by pushing himself beyond the boundaries of his comfort zone because his colleagues and his organization are depending upon him to rise above those inner limitations.

The self-belief we are describing is not arrogance – quite to the contrary. It is the self-belief of the level five servant leader described by Jim Collins, the paradoxical blend of a strong belief in one's own ability to accomplish big goals coupled with a genuine spirit of humility.

Self-Truth

"We come into this world with a specific, personal destiny. We have a job to do, a calling to enact, a self to become. We are who we are from the cradle, and we're stuck with it. Our job in this lifetime is not to shape ourselves into some ideal we imagine we ought to be, but to find out who we already are and become it."

Steven Pressfield: *The War of Art*

In the play Hamlet, Shakespeare had Polonius say that if you are true to yourself, you will never be false to anyone else. That is also true in reverse – if you are not being true to yourself, you will eventually not be true to others.

The statue "Self Made Man" by Colorado sculptor Bobbie Carlyle is of a man with a hammer in one hand and a chisel in the other who is carving himself out of a big block of stone. That is a beautiful metaphor for self-truth. It requires carving away those elements that reflect your lesser self (the part of you that often causes you to be your own worst enemy), and building upon your God-given strengths.

The nurse leader regularly takes time to reflect on his or her values, personal and professional development plans, and make midcourse corrections when needed. She is committed to being true to herself so that she will never be false to others.

Chapter Two

INTEGRITY

CORNERSTONES

Honesty

Reliability

Humility

Stewardship

Winning without integrity sets the stage for losing in ways that are far more important.

INTEGRITY

Character is destiny, and the foundation of character is integrity. Without integrity winning eventually leads to failure but with integrity losing becomes a platform for eventual success.

More than 2,500 years ago the Greek philosopher Heraclitus said that character is destiny. In recent years we have seen the profound truth of that statement as rich, famous and powerful people in the worlds of politics, sports, business, entertainment and even healthcare have been brought down by their own character flaws.

It's been said (by Abraham Lincoln and John Wooden, among others) that character is the tree and reputation is the shadow cast by that tree. The single-most vital quality of solid character strength is integrity – a commitment to doing the right thing even when it is hard, even when it is unpopular, even when it entails personal risk. Integrity is the value that earns trust and respect. It is the tree that creates the shadow cast by a trusted and respected nurse leader.

Ronald Greer gave his book on integrity the title *If You Know Who You Are You Will Know What to Do.* That is what the Danish minister Hendrick Kraemer told his parishioners when they came to him and asked whether, at great risk to themselves and their families, they should shelter Jews from the Nazi occupiers during the Second World War. That spirit captures the bridge between Core Action Value #1, Authenticity – knowing who you are, and Core Action Value #2, Integrity – knowing what to do (and then doing it).

Honesty

When you gain something by telling a lie, you lose something far more important. When you lose something by telling the truth, you gain something far more valuable.

For the nurse leader, honesty begins with self-honesty. Self-deception can take on many guises: denial, rationalization, procrastination, and blaming others for your problems are all forms of self-deception. As we noted in the previous chapter, Shakespeare's dictum that if you are true to yourself you will never be false to others is also true in reverse – if you are not being true to yourself you will eventually and inevitably be false to others.

Genuine honesty is, however, more than just refraining from telling lies. It is proactively living the truth – your truth. That can mean having the courage to have that dreaded confrontational conversation with someone who needs to be confronted; it can mean leaving the confines of your comfort zone to pursue higher education and become more active in your professional associations; and it can mean walking the talk yourself when you tell others to have a positive attitude about work, to take personal responsibility for their actions and outcomes, and to pursue a work-life balance. Nurse leaders develop trusting relationships with their associates to create a sustain a more positive workplace environment.

One more thing: recognize the difference between core principles and opinions. You should have a very limited number of immutable guiding principles, but lots of opinions that, no matter how strongly held, you are willing to change. Always remember that just because you believe something doesn't necessarily make it true, and just because you don't want to believe something doesn't necessarily make it false.

Reliability

The road to hell is not paved with good intentions. If there is such a road it is paved with broken promises, so be very judicious about letting your good intentions become cemented into committed promises.

This is our favorite definition of reliability: doing what you have promised to do, when you have promised to do it, and doing it to the very best of your abilities and resources.

The business mantras of "under-promise and over-deliver" and "exceed customer expectations" apply at the personal level as well. Do not make promises that you are not one-hundred percent committed to keep, then be determined to keep those promises sooner and better than any reasonable person would expect.

Procrastination is the ultimate enemy of reliability. Procrastination is putting off the work of today into the mists of tomorrow with the consequence that you are perpetually living under the shadow of what should have been done yesterday. The secret to overcoming procrastination is simple, though not always easy: just say no (to tempting diversions and distractions); just do it (to the very best of your ability); and do it now (eat your live toad first thing in the morning and the rest of your day will assuredly get better from that point on).

Humility

Leadership authority Jim Collins defines level five leadership as being a paradoxical blend of an incredibly strong commitment to achieve important goals coupled with a very genuine sense of personal humility. The leaders we most admire (think of Abraham Lincoln) embody these qualities.

W e do not trust people who are arrogant and narcissistic. They tend to listen only to radio station WIIFM (What's In It For Me?) and their decisions are guided primarily by their own self-interest. They do not seek, and will not accept, genuine feedback or constructive criticism. Their hubris – the pride that comes before the fall – often sets the stage for eventual failure, or catastrophe.

The root of the word integrity is integer, which in mathematics means one indivisible whole. In human terms that means, as Mother Teresa put it, that we are all children of the same God. The nurse leader with heart appreciates that regardless of the costume that someone happens to wear to work, we are all sacred beings deserving of the same respect and dignity.

Because there is no humility gene, this is something that we must conscientiously work to nurture. The nurse leader with heart learns to give credit when things go well and to accept responsibility when they do not go well; to accept and listen to others without prejudging or making assumptions; to look past superficial appearances and stereotypes; and to laugh loudest when the joke is on her. After all, the words humor and humility share the same root.

Stewardship

---

*"We don't own the earth, we
are borrowing it from
our grandchildren."*

Chief Seattle

This quote captures the essence of the stewardship obligation. It is a matter of integrity that we honor our obligation to future generations.

At the personal level, this means taking care of our health and our finances so that we do not become burdens upon our families or upon society, and so that we are able to leave the legacy we were put on this earth to create.

At the organizational level, this means that we do our best to eliminate waste and to optimize efficiency and productivity so that healthcare resources will be optimally available and accessible in the years to come.

And at the environmental level it means that we do our part to pass down the beautiful earth it has been our blessing to occupy to our children and their children and grandchildren.

We should always strive to leave our organizations and the people we work with better than when we arrived. That is stewardship in action.

Chapter Three

AWARENESS

CORNERSTONES

Mindfulness

Objectivity

Empathy

Reflection

Learn from the past, plan for the future, but live in the present. If you're not enjoying the journey, the destination will be a disappointment.

AWARENESS

*Awareness is the key to a successful
and rewarding experience in virtually
every dimension of life – as a parent, as a
caregiver, as a professional,
as a leader, as a citizen, and
as a human being.*

In her classic work *Notes on Nursing: What It Is and What It Is Not*, Florence Nightingale wrote that to be a good nurse it is not enough for one to be caring and compassionate. To be a good nurse, she said, the nurse must also be acutely aware of her patient's condition and surroundings.

For the nurse leader, this mandate of awareness is broadened to having the ability to be acutely aware of the attitudes and behaviors of the people for whom, and to whom, she is responsible, as well as being aware of what is going on in the environment. The "5 whys" technique for total quality management is an effective tool for enhancing personal awareness. With each subsequent "Why?" he penetrates beneath superficial appearances toward genuine awareness and understanding.

Of course, every question we ask and every decision we make is filtered through the lens of our own ego, emotions, and ambitions. To be an effective nurse leader also requires awareness of how these inner conditions can distort our perceptions of outer realities.

Mindfulness

Learn from the past, plan for the future, but live in the present and do not allow yourself to be crushed between the anvil of yesterday's regrets and the hammer of tomorrow's fears.

Past and future are bookends; it is in the present that the real story is being written every day. But in today's world, where there are so many competing demands clamoring for our limited attention, living mindfully in the present is harder than ever. Your attention is your most precious resource because it is so finite and limited. We ask people to "pay" attention, not to "lend" attention, precisely because we are asking them to give up this most non-renewable of resources.

One of the best personal investments a nurse leader can make is a consistent practice of mindfulness. By devoting 15-20 minutes per day in your facility's chapel, healing garden, walking labyrinth, or other venue that was established for this purpose, you will not only enhance your own powers of mind and mindfulness, you will also set an example for others, and give them permission to follow that example.

Mindfulness is also about being present in meetings, conversations with the people we work with and with family and friends at home. It often means setting aside preoccupations and fixing our awareness on the present that is right in front of us. Remember: present is also a synonym for gift.

Objectivity

To be objective is to see things
as they really are – not as they used to be,
as they should be, as you wish they were,
or as you fear they might become – but
as they really are.

It's human nature, but because we are all human we tend to form our opinions first and then to seek out the facts that reinforce those opinions. It takes courage and humility to say, "You might be right" or "I could be wrong" or "I had not looked at it that way" but being willing to look at something from someone else's viewpoint is essential to being truly objective.

Especially for someone in a leadership position, it is also important to distrust first impressions, labels, and stereotypes. We had a vivid firsthand experience of this while doing research for our book *Building a Culture of Ownership in Healthcare*. One day we interviewed chief nursing officers at two different hospitals. The first CNO complained that millennials had a poor work ethic and lacked any sense of loyalty to the organization. The second CNO told us that they were actively seeking out millennials because they were passionate and often had natural leadership qualities.

Now, both CNOs were obviously making significant generalizations based upon the label of millennial, but which one do you think will have a better track record at recruiting and retaining members of the millennial generation?

Empathy

*We tend to judge ourselves mostly
by our good intentions, but others
will judge us based upon our actions.
Meanwhile, others are judging themselves
based upon their good intentions while
we are judging them based
upon their actions.*

The late Mary Kay Ash used to tell her beauty consultants (not salespeople – beauty consultants) that they should imagine everyone they'd meet wearing a sign that said MMFI – Make Me Feel Important. Alcoholics Anonymous adheres to the principle of mutuality, referring to the fact that the recovering drunk's sponsor needs the drunk every bit as much as the drunk needs his or her sponsor.

The technical definition of empathy is the ability to feel someone else's emotions, but for the nurse leader there is a higher standard. Empathy is not just being able to put yourself in someone else's shoes – it is making that other person feel special and creating a bond of mutual acceptance and compassion.

The Cleveland Clinic's empathy videos brilliantly capture the fact that regardless of outside appearances, everyone has a story – and everyone deserves our empathy. We believe that anyone who can watch those videos and not be emotionally moved should find a field of work other than healthcare.

Reflection

---

*You will never find time for personal
reflection, you must make it a routine
discipline because, to paraphrase Socrates,
the examined life will be
far more rewarding and fulfilled
than the unexamined life.*

There is always a gap between what you say your values are and how those values are actually reflected in your calendar, your checkbook register, the decisions you make and the relationships you create. The challenge in life is to recognize that gap and continuously work to narrow it.

Unfortunately, as executive coach Marshall Goldsmith describes in his book *What Got You Here Won't Get You There*, we are almost always the last to be aware when there is a disconnect between what we say are our values and the attitudes and behaviors that others see in us. That is why it is imperative that the nurse leader actively solicit feedback and be sincerely receptive to constructive criticisms.

But it is also important for leaders to make time for reflection and introspection, and the best time for doing that is the golden hour of each day – the first and the last 30 minutes. In the morning, before you check email or read the headlines, take 30 minutes for reflection, introspection, prayer and for visualizing the day in front of you. Then at night, just before you go to bed, turn off the television and stow away the cell phone and devote your last 30 waking minutes to thinking about how your day went, and what you could have done to make it go better, and planning your activities and priorities for the next day.

Chapter Four

COURAGE

_____

CORNERSTONES

Confrontation

Transformation

Action

Connection

Fear is a reaction, courage is a decision.

COURAGE

Courage, said Winston Churchill, is the most important of all virtues because it is the one that makes all the other virtues possible. C.S. Lewis took that one step farther by saying that courage is all of the other virtues at the point where they are tested. It's easy to have integrity where there is no temptation, and it's easy to be brave when there is no danger. It takes courage to live one's values.

In his book *The Road Less Traveled*, Dr. Scott Peck wrote that the absence of fear is not courage – the absence of fear is brain damage! Fear is a natural, hardwired human condition. Fear can be your greatest enemy by paralyzing you from taking necessary action. Or it can be your greatest ally by catalyzing you to take that necessary action.

Unfortunately, fear can also be a profoundly devastating learning disability. People who don't ask questions for fear of looking dumb never learn. People who don't try for fear of failure never grow. People who never ask for fear of rejection never gain. People who fear the uncertainty of change stagnate.

You might have heard that the acronym FEAR stands for Fantasized Evidence Appearing Real. When it prevents you from taking necessary action, it is also a Fabulous Excuse for Avoiding Responsibility. As a nurse leader, it is your responsibility to bravely confront your fears and do the things that are important, scary though they might be.

Confrontation

"He who has conquered doubt and fear has conquered failure. His every thought is allied with power, and all difficulties are bravely met and wisely overcome... Thought allied fearlessly to purpose becomes creative force."

James Allen:
As A Man Thinketh

The first step to overcoming fear is to confront it head-on. As Eleanor Roosevelt said, "You gain strength, courage and confidence by every experience in which you really stop to look fear in the face."

Scratch any negative emotion or self-sabotaging behavior deeply enough and at the bottom you will find fear. Low self-esteem is often caused by fear of not measuring up and worry about what others might think of us. Procrastination is fueled by fear of undesirable outcomes (or on our laziest days, fear of hard work). Managerial abdication is fueled by fear of confrontation.

As in medicine, when it comes to taking courageous action, diagnosis the first step to effective treatment. Defining your fears as clearly as possible will guide you toward the actions you must take to overcome those fears. As a nurse leader you must, as Eleanor Roosevelt admonished, look fear in the face and do the things that you know must be done but which cause you apprehension.

Transformation

The physical symptoms of terror and exhilaration are identical. The only difference is the name you give to the symptoms. The challenge of leadership is to help people transform the paralyzing power of fear into the catalyzing power of courage.

Caring is the root of fear. The reason one fears is because they care. If you didn't care what other people thought of you, you wouldn't fear having those tough conversations with people who are underperforming or damaging your unit's morale with their toxically negative attitudes. If you didn't care about whether or not anyone ever read the book that you are planning to write "someday maybe" then you would not fear rejection.

Caring is also the root of courage. When you care enough about the emotional climate of your workplace and its impact on your colleagues and the patients and patients' family members that you serve, you will find the courage to have those courageous conversations. When you care enough about the subject of your book-to-be, then you will find the courage to face the likelihood of rejection and keep writing.

Wednesday's Promise of The Self Empowerment Pledge is Determination. It says, "I will do the things I'm afraid to do but which I know should be done. Sometimes this will mean asking for help to do that which I cannot do by myself." Internalizing that promise into the DNA of your personal character will help you transform paralyzing fear into galvanizing courage.

Action

Action is the hacksaw that cuts through the prison bars of fear. Action is the difference between wishful thinking (hoping for something and waiting for someone else to make it happen) and positive thinking (expecting something and working to make it happen).

In *The Analects*, Confucius is quoted as saying, "To see what is right and not to do it is cowardice." Having the courage to act and do the things you are afraid to do is the difference between having unfulfilled good intentions and making a difference.

One of the biggest mistakes a leader can make is waiting for fear to go away. The fear does not go away. Fear, as reflected in the fight-or-flight reflex, is programmed into your DNA. Indeed, the longer you put off acting in the face of your fears, the more terrifying they are likely to become. This is important to understand, because while fear is an emotion, courage is making the decision to overcome that emotion. People who do brave things do not feel courageous. The person who runs in front of a speeding truck to push someone out of harm's way does not feel courage – they feel fear and still do what needs to be done. Being afraid is okay. Letting fear paralyze you is not okay.

One more thing. The difference between crazy and courageous is often evident only in retrospect. The people who tell you that you are crazy to be taking a risk today will be the ones standing on the sidelines applauding when that risk pays off. Take the advice of Susan Jeffers from her book of this title: feel the fear and do it anyway.

Connection

---

*Fear breeds in isolation; courage
is nurtured through connection.
One of the nurse leader's paramount
responsibilities is to foster a culture
where there is a spirit of mutual
support and fellowship in
the workplace.*

Did you see the movie *Castaway* where Tom Hanks played a man who was stranded on a desert island for more than five years? There were no other humans on the island, but as the story progresses we see Hanks bonding with Wilson, the volleyball. By movie's end Wilson is his best friend, his closest confidant, his soulmate. The need for human connection, for fellowship, is so profoundly programmed into our genes that if there are no people around we will manufacture that fellowship out of an inanimate object.

Nobody understands the emotional power of fellowship better than the marketing geniuses at the Coca Cola company. Coke ads *never* talk about fizzy brown sugar water that will make you fat and eventually kill you. The little boy and Mean Joe Green, teaching the world to sing, paying it forward – the most memorable Coke ads are all about human connection.

We have both spent many evenings and weekends with friends who are struggling and support groups for strangers who are struggling. People come together because they are addicts, or because of a shared medical diagnosis, or because of losses in common. When the conversations end, the participants are still alcoholics, they still have cancer, and their lost loved ones are not coming back to them. But they have a little more hope, a new friend, a new idea. They are encouraged – they have gained a new spirit of courage – from that human connection. We often wonder what it would take to create that support group sort of feel in the workplace. It begins with having the courage to connect.

Chapter Five

PERSEVERANCE

———————————————

CORNERSTONES

Preparation

Perspective

Toughness

Learning

Fear is a reaction, courage is a decision. Perseverance is making that decision day after day – it is courage that endures.

PERSEVERANCE

"Brick walls are not there to stop you, they are there to make you prove how much you want something."

Randy Pausch
The Last Lecture

One of our favorite sayings on perseverance is that everything can look like a failure in the middle. When any new initiative is launched there is a high level of enthusiasm, and when you cross the finish line there is a sense of accomplishment. It's somewhere in the middle – the proverbial twentieth mile of a marathon, the valley of the shadow – that exhaustion and despair can set in and derail the project.

Joseph Campbell, the great scholar of the power of myth, wrote about the hero's journey. The hero sets off on a grand quest (enthusiasm at the beginning). In a desperate fight with a fierce dragon he falls off his horse, loses his sword in the mud, and the dragon hovers above him breathing fire (apparent failure in the middle). But somehow the hero retrieves his sword, slays the dragon, and rescues the princess. They ride off into the sunset to live happily ever after.

That, said Campbell, is the universal story. It is the story of *The Odyssey*, of *Star Wars*, and of *The Lord of the Rings*. It is the story of raising children, of finishing nursing school, of writing a book. It is our story and it is your story. And it is the role of the nurse leader to sustain our courage and determination when, to all outside appearances, the battle seems to have been lost.

Preparation

When the body is strong it will bend to your commands. When the body is weak, you must give in to its demands.

The Samurai Paradox

Bad things happen to good people. Harold Kushner told us that in his book of that title. Note that he did not say *if* bad things happen – he said *when* bad things happen. Every one of us will struggle with bad things happening in our personal and in our professional lives. And every organization will struggle with staffing, financial, technological, competitive, and other challenges. Consider it to be a law of the universe.

When Friedrich Nietzsche wrote that what doesn't kill you will make you stronger (a phrase popularized in a contemporary song by Kelly Clarkson), he did not mean to say that growing stronger through adversity is spontaneous or inevitable. One of the most important ways to assure that adversity will make us stronger when it, inevitably, arrives is to be prepared for it.

Because no one can be sure when adversity will strike, or what form it will take when it does, the nurse leader prepares the way a fire department prepares for the next fire. Since the fire chief never knows what form the next fire will take, he trains his crew generically for the specific. The nurse leader can do the same with her team. By helping her people grow stronger as professionals and as persons, she helps to assure that they will weather whatever storms the world throws at them – at work or at home.

That is one reason we are big fans of the Healthy Nurse, Healthy Nation Great Challenge launched by the American Nurses Association. Healthy nurses are stronger, more resilient, and more likely to persevere when, as Rabbi Kushner assures us they will, bad things happen to us good people.

Perspective

Is it the best of times or the worst of times? Our answer is always the same – Yes! Despite the challenges in today's healthcare environment, every day medical miracles are taking place. The effective nurse leader keeps a focus on the positive and an optimistic perspective for the future.

The Pickle Pledge reminds us that buried inside every complaint there is either a blessing or a constructive suggestion. Reduced reimbursements challenge us to be more cost-effective. The nursing shortage challenges us to do a better job of retaining our best people. A new crosstown competitor challenges us to do a better job of creating a magnificent patient experience. And responding to our complaints by remembering The Pickle Pledge can also remind us that we should be a little more grateful for the blessings that we do have.

That you tend to get out of life what you expect isn't just a trite saying – it is a scientifically documented phenomenon. It is the underlying basis of the Placebo Effect, the Pygmalion Effect, and the Hawthorne Effect. What you choose to see today, and how you choose to interpret what you see, will have a profound influence on your expectations for the future.

Whether or not to have a positive perspective is a choice that we all make every day. In fact, it is a choice we make many times a day. It is also a habit and a discipline – a commitment to conscientiously find the blessings and the constructive suggestions in every problem.

---

* The Pickle Pledge says, "I will turn every complaint into either a blessing or a constructive suggestion." For more information see our book *Pickle Pledge* and visit www.PicklePledge.com.

Toughness

Every great accomplishment was once the "impossible" dream of a dreamer who refused to quit when confronted with brick walls. The bigger the dream, the higher and thicker will be the walls.

When Ernest Shackleton's ship *Endurance* was first trapped in and then crushed by Antarctic ice in 1916, one of his most daunting challenges was to maintain the morale of his 28 crew members during their 634-day ordeal. Shackleton knew his first duty was to maintain hope and optimism, and to stave off despair, no matter how desperate the situation might seem. In retrospect, one can speculate on how frequently members of the crew were tempted to quit before the breakthrough that led to their rescue. He later wrote: "I have marveled often at the thin line that divides success from failure and the sudden turn that leads from apparently certain disaster to comparative safety."

When Bob's team at Midland Memorial Hospital learned that – after all the blood, sweat, tears, and love they had put into the process – their Magnet application had not been approved, his first job was to help re-inspire the team's confidence, help them put the swagger back into their steps. He had to convince them that this brick wall would not stop them, it would make them stronger, and that their next application would be successful. He reminded them that one of the core values of Midland Health is Pioneer Spirit and that, like the pioneers who first settled in West Texas, they had to have the toughness to persevere through to success.

Positive enthusiasm and mental toughness are hardest to find at precisely those times where they are most important, which is why it's essential to cultivate the underlying strength of character before it's required. The fact that every member of the team had completed the course on The Twelve Core Action Values, and that several were in fact Certified Values Coach Trainers, made Bob's job much easier.

Learning

---

*"If only it were possible for us to
see farther than our knowledge reaches,
and even a little beyond the outworks of
our presentiment, perhaps we would
bear our sadness with greater trust
than we have in our joys. For they are the
moments when something new has entered
us, something unknown."*

Rainer Maria Rilke:
Letters to a Young Poet

Nobody looks forward to having bad things happen, but whether we want it or not, bad things do happen. Here are for good things that can happen when bad things happen:

Benefit #1: Times of difficulty are essential to build character. Think of your own challenging past experiences – do any of them now strike you as the best thing that could have happened because you are stronger as a result?

Benefit #2: We learn more from failure than we do from success. In his book *Zen Guitar*, Philip Toshio Sudo wrote: "Use your mistakes as a springboard into new areas of discovery; accidents can hold the key to innovation. When things fall apart, make art." One of the key precepts of just culture is learning from mistakes rather than seeking to blame people for making them.

Benefit #3: Adversity can open doors and identify opportunities. Some of the most effective and compassionate counselors and caregivers are those who through their own adversity opened the door to helping others.

Benefit #4: Times of adversity are often when we meet the people who end up being most important in our lives. Perhaps this is because when we are vulnerable the emotional walls come down and we are more open to making a personal connection.

Chapter Six

FAITH

___

CORNERSTONES

Gratitude

Forgiveness

Love

Spirituality

Faith is a force that is just beginning at the
point where certainty ends.

FAITH

*My faith and my gratitude for
all that I have been blessed with will
shine through in my attitudes
and in my actions.*

*Sunday's Promise of
The Self Empowerment Pledge*

When we talk about faith as a value, we are not talking about religion. We're talking about the sort of faith that *everyone* needs, regardless of their religious belief or non-belief. We think of the four pillars of faith as being faith in yourself, faith in other people, faith in the future, and faith in a power that is beyond what can be seen with the eye but only felt in the heart.

Faith can also be seen as the marriage of fidelity and trust. Fidelity is being faithful to a person, a cause, a profession, or an organization. Trust is having faith in other people, in organizations, and in the future.

Especially in healthcare, it is essential that we separate notions of faith from articles of religious belief, allowing all people to worship, or not worship, in their own chosen ways; in this we follow the example that Florence Nightingale set in her work at the Scutari Barrack Hospital where she insisted that clinical triage be on the basis of the patient's medical condition and not their religion.

In her book *A Simple Path*, Mother Teresa wrote that we are all children of the same God. As a nurse leader, whether you are working in a secular or a religiously affiliated organization, it is your obligation to assure that all patients are treated with the same high level of respect and dignity, and that their own beliefs be honored, whether or not they are the same as the beliefs held by the caregiver.

Gratitude

---

*Gratitude is measured in minutes
while resentment is measured in years;
an attitude of gratitude will
elevate your altitude.*

Gratitude is a central tenet of many of the world's major spiritual traditions. We give thanks for our daily bread and we give to others from a spirit of gratitude for our own many blessings. A sense of gratitude is good for your health at every level – physical, emotional and spiritual. And gratitude for the blessings of today is the platform for optimism about the future – if you aren't grateful for what you have now, what on earth makes you think that things will change so that you are grateful at some later time?

One of the most important expressions of gratitude the nurse leader can give is for the people who report to her. It is a strange paradox that healthcare, of all professions, has historically had a culture where doing excellent work was "just doing my job" and managers have been reluctant to praise people for "just doing their job" in an outstanding manner. Fortunately, this is changing – partly with the stimulus of external programs like the DAISY Award to recognize extraordinary nurses – but there is much room for progress. "Thank you" and "I appreciate you" are words that are heard too infrequently in many healthcare organizations.

The antithesis of gratitude is resentment. That's one of the reasons that we are both fully committed to promoting The Pickle Pledge and The Pickle Challenge to eliminate whining and complaining from the workplace environment. Complaining almost always reflects a lack of gratitude. Learning to be thankful for what you have and search for ways to make things better whenever you are tempted to complain can be a life-changing discipline.

Forgiveness

"Forgiveness is a skill, a way of preserving clarity, sanity and generosity in an individual life, a beautiful way of shaping the mind to a future we want for ourselves... To forgive is to put oneself in a larger gravitational field of experience than the one that first seemed to hurt us."

David Whyte: Consolations: The Solace, Nourishment and Underlying Meaning of Everyday Words

This is ancient wisdom: hatred is a chain that binds you to the object of your hatred, and carrying a grudge is like drinking poison in hopes of hurting someone else. Forgiveness is another central tenet of many spiritual traditions. In The Lord's Prayer, the requested forgiveness is bilateral: the petitioner, "forgive us our trespasses as we forgive those who trespass against us." Of course, the real beneficiary of our willingness to forgive is not the person who is being forgiven, who might not care less, but we ourselves in being relieved of the burden of that anger, hatred and grief.

At the organizational level forgiveness is often a prerequisite for progress. Many organizations have what we think of as "institutional PTSD." People hang onto the old dramas, they tell and re-tell the old stories, in a way that prevents meaningful progress into the future. They hang onto dreadful stories of the previous leader rather than assuming good faith on the part of that person's replacement. Nurse leaders must forgive and let go of dramas from the past or their grudges will fester and they will falter.

Prospective forgiveness is the antidote to cynicism. The cynic assumes that others are acting in bad faith. To practice prospective forgiveness is to assume that others are acting in good faith unless and until their actions prove otherwise.

Love

The Beatles had it right: there's nothing you can do that can't be done, all you need is love. They also had it right when they sang that the love you take is equal to the love you make, and that it's within you and without you.

Work is "love made visible" in the memorable phrase of Kahlil Gibran in his lovely book *The Prophet*. And nowhere is the obligation to make work "love made visible" more imperative than in the healing professions. If more healthcare workplaces had that spirit, the American Nurses Association would not have found it necessary to adopt a white paper on bullying and incivility in the workplace, nor would the Tri-Council for Nursing have found it necessary to create and disseminate the Nursing Civility Proclamation, which we have included in Appendix 4.

As Scott Peck pointed out in his book *The Road Less Traveled*, real love is not just a mushy emotion – it is hard work and sacrifice on behalf of the one you love. If the drunk at the bar crying in his whiskey about how much he loves his family really did love them, he'd sober up, get a job, and help his kids get through college.

One more thing. Norman Vincent Peele reminded his readers that the great commandment says to "Love your neighbor as yourself," and that we should not forget those last two words. It's often said that you cannot pour out of an empty pitcher, and the caregiver needs to take care of his or herself so that they can take care of others. Or as singer Bonnie Raitt put it (in more earthy terms) in one of her songs, "a man could never love me who can't even love himself."

Spirituality

Spirituality is honoring the spirit, in yourself and in others. It is the emotional underpinning of gratitude, of forgiveness, of love, and of a life with meaning. For the nurse leader, the act of inspiring others is a gift of the spirit.

In the context of personal values, being spiritual is not the same as being religious. It is being open to the miracles that we can see all around us if we are paying attention. Spirituality is the ability to experience awe at the amazing miracle of the human body, and of our ability to mend it when it needs mending; to experience wonder at the transcendent beauty of the natural world; to be deeply touched by a baby's smile or a mother's tears; to sense that there is more to the world than can be seen with the eyes, and more to life than dying with the most toys.

The heart of a nurse leader guides her to see beyond the job description of a colleague and to empathize with the human being on the other side of the nametag. Especially in healthcare, leadership with heart is about more than just achieving business growth and professional growth – it is also about inspiring (in-spiriting) spiritual growth.

Much has been written about how the soul of our healing professions has been imperiled by the encroachment of big businesses practices in healthcare systems. The fact that healthcare is now a big business will never be reversed, and in fact is more likely to accelerate. This makes it all the more important for the nurse leader to protect and nurture the spirit of her people and the soul of her organization.

CORE ACTION VALUES 7-12

The Power for
Making a Difference

1. Purpose

2. Vision

3. Focus

4. Enthusiasm

5. Service

6. Leadership

Chapter Seven

PURPOSE

CORNERSTONES

Aspiration

Intentionality

Selflessness

Balance

Someone with a job is never secure; someone with
a purpose is never unemployed.

PURPOSE

*The work that you choose to do,
and the attitude with which you choose
to do that work, are the most important
decisions you will ever make – make
sure that you make these
choices on purpose.*

Mark Twain said that the two most important days in a person's life are the day you are born and the day you figure out why. Some people are fortunate in having a calling come calling early in life, the way Florence Nightingale felt her call to be a nurse as a young woman sitting under a tree on her father's estate. For the rest of us, though, finding a life's purpose often entails much hit-or-miss, trial-and-error. We might find that over the course of a lifetime, we have more than one "calling" – perhaps many more than one.

Sometimes our true purpose becomes clear only in the face of great adversity. In their book *Nursing in the Storm* Denise Danna and Sandra Cordray share stories of nurses who cared for others during Hurricane Katrina. Dan Kiff had been a nurse for 18 years, but he said that his service during Katrina was "the wake-up call to me that this… is what I was put on this earth to do." His was one of many such stories we've heard from nurses going above and beyond the call of their job descriptions during disaster situations.

To do something "on purpose" means to do it with commitment, pride and enthusiasm. It means to treat your work as "love made visible." Whatever your hand finds to do, do it with all your might (Ecclesiastes 9:10). That is working with purpose.

Aspiration

Aspire to great achievement and work on becoming the person you need to be to achieve those great goals – then inspire the people you lead to do the same thing.

One of the six core values of the Iowa-based Clickstop corporation is "Expect greatness in yourself and inspire it in others." In his book *Healing Children*, Dr. Kurt Newman, CEO of Children's National Health System in Washington DC, writes about how when caring for children, caregivers must also consider the adult that child will someday become. He says, "creative childhood treatments are now geared toward transforming the adulthood awaiting each child." Using an aphorism that was shared with him by a patient, he says that you can never tell how far a frog will jump.

That is a great metaphor for aspirational leadership. Nurse leaders should help others see in themselves their greatest potential and then commit to fulfilling that potential – to be the frog that jumps farther than anyone would have thought possible. To expect greatness in themselves and to inspire it in others.

People who aspire greatly are often warned against having false hope (we suppose they would rather that people have genuine pessimism and despair). Our answer to that is there is no such thing as false hope. Check out Joe's video on The Hope Diamond at the link below, featuring music by Grammy Award winning pianist Laura Sullivan.

Note: We hope it's obvious that when we refer to aspiration in the context of values, we're talking about ambition, and not the clinical definition of the term.

 or google "The Hope Diamond Video"

Intentionality

No one can empower you but you – it is an inside job. But once you have empowered yourself, no one can take that power away from you.

Peter Drucker, the man who is credited with inventing modern management, said that wherever great things are being done, behind the scenes there is "a monomaniac with a mission." Intentionality is the fuel that inspires a bias for action, which is consistently rated as one of the hallmark qualities of a successful organization. Intentionality is the difference between wishful thinking (hoping for something and waiting for someone else to make it happen) and positive thinking (expecting something and doing the work to make it happen).

The nurse leader who is intentional does not allow obstacles to become excuses and does not allow cynicism and passive-aggressive resistance to poison the team's optimism.

These are challenging times in healthcare, and challenging times call for intentional leaders at every level of the organization. The Culture of Ownership Classroom at Midland Memorial Hospital has a large banner with the words Proceed Until Apprehended*. Those three words capture the spirit of intentionality – a commitment to getting things done instead of hoping and waiting for someone else to do the work of doing the right thing – always.

* Taken from Joe's book *The Florence Prescription: From Accountability to Ownership*

Selflessness

"Individuals committed to a vision beyond their self-interest find they have energy not available when pursuing narrower goals, as will organizations that tap this level of commitment."

Peter Senge: The Fifth Discipline

Committing oneself to the healing professions requires a selfless commitment to caring for others. For the nurse leader, this means making a commitment to the personal and professional growth and development of followers. It means being a coach and a mentor, not just a boss. Through the example she sets for others, the nurse leader imbues her colleagues with the same spirit of selflessness.

Here's the ultimate paradox of selfless leadership: by demonstrating their commitment to a cause that transcends personal self-interest and to prioritizing the success of others ahead of their own, selfless leaders earn the respect, trust and loyalty of followers that ultimately leads to a level of success far greater than they could possibly have achieved on their own by pursuing success directly. It is a law of the universe: Whatever you most need in life, the best way for you to get it is to help someone else get it who needs it more than you do.

The opening words of Rick Warren's book *The Purpose Driven Life* are "It's not about you." For the nurse leader, it's about patients, coworkers, and the community. It's about doing the right thing and making a contribution. But by the beautiful paradox of selflessness, it is true that as you give so too shall you receive.

Balance

Our lives are never, and never can be, in perfect balance. The challenge is making sure that the scales are always tipped toward the things that really matter at the times when they matter most.

One of the qualities that leadership authority Jim Collins finds in organizations that achieve and sustain greatness is a determination to replace "the tyranny of or" with "the genius of and." Instead of giving in to the tyranny of low cost *or* high quality, they demand both. Instead of giving in to the tyranny of high morale *or* high productivity, the insist upon both.

To be a nurse leader is a demanding calling that often requires intense commitment and long hours. To achieve balance does not mean making sure that the scales are always evenly balanced between work and personal life. It means not letting the "tyranny of or" prevent you from caring for yourself and making time for your family by creatively seeking "genius of and" solutions. This often means training, and then trusting, your colleagues to do the work that right now only you can do.

In his book *Life and Work*, James Autrey suggested that rather than trying to *balance* your life and your work as if they were two separate weights at opposite ends of a scale, you seek to *integrate* your life and your work. Good advice, that.

Chapter Eight

VISION

CORNERSTONES

Attention

Imagination

Articulation

Belief

Humans are the only creatures who have been blessed with the gift of being able to see things not just as they are but as they might be, and with the power to transform those dreams of today into the realities of tomorrow.

VISION

"If one advances confidently in the direction of his dreams, and endeavors to live the life which he has imagined, he will meet with a success unexpected in common hours... If you have built castles in the air, your work need not be lost; that is where they should be. Now put the foundations under them."

Henry David Thoreau: Walden

Vision, said author Jonathan Swift, is the art of seeing the invisible. An architect can "see" the visible architecture of a building even before the foundation has been laid. He builds castles in the air, then puts foundations under them with renderings and blueprints.

Especially in healthcare organizations, the employee and the patient experience are far more affected by what we call the Invisible Architecture* of core values, organizational culture, and workplace attitude than they are by the visible architecture of bricks and mortar. Using the power of vision, the nurse leader can create a shared image of the ideal culture for her organization, or her part of the organization.

Creating that shared vision is an iterative exercise. Vision is the noun – visualization is the verb. A shared vision is the outcome of a process of visualization. Just as the architect progresses from rough schematics through detailed renderings and construction blueprints, so too the nurse leader creates a vision of the ideal workplace culture by engaging people in a dialog about mutual desires, expectations, and commitments.

Invisible Architecture™ is a trademark of Values Coach Inc.

Attention

---

*What you choose to pay attention
to in the present will be the platform
upon which you build your
dreams of the future.*

When someone is asking for your attention, they do not ask you to *lend* attention – they ask you to *pay* attention. Your attention is the ultimately non-renewable resource. You can only pay attention to one thing at a time (no, you cannot multitask attention), and once your attention has been paid it cannot be deposited back into your account. Ralph Waldo Emerson famously said that "a man becomes what he thinks about all day long." The things that you choose to pay attention to today will profoundly influence the goals you achieve, and the person you become, in the future.

For the nurse leader, attention has both an exterior and an interior dimension. The exterior dimension means paying attention to the world around you, being alert to potential problems and opportunities. Someone paying attention at a grocery store saw the potential of applying barcodes to pharmaceuticals, thus making healthcare safer; someone paying attention to line management at Disneyworld found creative ways to make emergency room wait times more bearable.

The interior dimension is just as important, and often more so. That is paying attention to how your own preconceived assumptions and self-talk color your perceptions of what you see in other people and in the world around you. Not allowing your own negative self-talk or fear of uncertainty to prevent you from pursuing positive change. Knowing the triggers that cause you to react in ways that you will later regret and pulling the plug before they detonate. Knowing yourself, minute by minute.

Imagination

Dream a big dream, make it a
memory of the future, and
expect a miracle

Through the power of imagination, you can remember the future more clearly and accurately than you can remember the past. To prove it to yourself, try to recall your second birthday. Now visualize a mental picture of where you will be and what you will be doing tomorrow. This is a great illustration of the way we are overconfident in the accuracy of our memories but sell short the power of vision. The secret of success is to remember a tomorrow that is somehow different, and better, than yesterday – and not just tomorrow but next week and next year.

Imagination is the gift we use to see things that are not actually there – at least not yet. it is the catalyst for self-fulfilling prophecies. As children we exercise this gift in play and in conversations with imaginary friends. Unfortunately, as we grow up we tend to warp our imaginations with worry and fantasy. Worry is imagining bad things that you did not want to have happen, while fantasy (aka magical thinking) is imagining wonderful things happening without a concomitant commitment to doing the work to make those things happen.

Imagination is a mental muscle. Like every other muscle it grows stronger when it's used, and it atrophies when it is not used. It is for the nurse leader to challenge the team to imagine in a positive and constructive way. One of the most powerful ways to spark the creativity of your team is to start with a sentence beginning with the words "Imagine a world that is..." or "Imagine a workplace where people..." and then see where the conversation leads.

Articulation

*Define your future by
your hopes
and not by your fears,
by your dreams
and not by your memories.*

B efore a dream can become real, it must be articulated in a way that informs and inspires the people whose commitment is necessary to make it happen. The dream of a new home must be articulated in a blueprint for the contractor and a set of financial documents for the banker. Martin Luther King articulated his dream of a world free from racial prejudice and hate in one of history's most memorable speeches, but also in his 7,000-word Letter from the Birmingham Jail. Each articulation was crafted for its unique audience.

For the nurse leader, articulating a vision often means crafting mental images that create a visceral emotional response. In our book *Pickle Pledge: Creating a More Positive Healthcare Workplace One Attitude at a Time*, we called toxic emotional negativity the emotional and spiritual equivalent of cigarette smoke in the workplace. We wanted that simple but powerful word picture to reinforce commitment to a positive culture by showing that bullying, incivility, and other forms of toxically negative attitudes and behaviors are just as corrosive to colleagues' souls as cigarette smoke in the air is to their bodies.

The most powerful way to articulate the desired culture is with stories and symbols. The story of how Mary Kay Ash founded her cosmetics company after having been passed over for promotion by less qualified men has inspired thousands of Mary Kay Beauty Consultants to aspire to earn a bumblebee pin. This was an important metaphor for Mary Kay, because according to aerodynamic theory, a bumblebee should not be able to fly. Don't ever tell that to a bumblebee, she would say, and do not ever let anyone tell you that you cannot fly.

Belief

Have a dream so big that the only way you will ever be able to achieve it is by becoming a bigger person yourself.

In his book *Flight to Arras*, Antoine de Saint-Exupery wrote: "A rock pile ceases to be a rock pile the moment a single man contemplates it, bearing within him the image of a cathedral." In medicine, the power of belief has been thoroughly documented in studies on the Placebo Effect, which has been estimated to account for a third or more of positive therapeutic outcomes. Likewise, the power of belief underlies the Hawthorne Effect in business and the Pygmalion Effect in personal development.

Belief in the vision of something better is an incredible source of motivation, and can power the team through the inevitable obstacles and setbacks along the way. One of the nurse leader's most important responsibilities is nurturing and sustaining collective belief during those challenging times, the way Franklin Delano Roosevelt restored belief of the American people that reminding them that "we have nothing to fear but fear itself" during the darkest days of the Great Depression, and that Winston Churchill bolstered belief of the British people by promising them that "we shall never surrender" during the darkest days of the Nazi blitz.

Walt Disney said, "If you can dream it you can do it." Napoleon Hill added the essential catalytic ingredient when he wrote, "What the mind of man can conceive *and believe* the body of man can achieve" (emphasis in original, as is the unenlightened gender-specific language).

Chapter Nine

FOCUS

———

CORNERSTONES

Target

Concentration

Speed

Momentum

Keeping a focus on what matters most is an essential
skill for your career and professional development and
ultimately for your personal success and happiness; keeping a
team focused on what matters most is an essential skill
for achieving important goals.

FOCUS

*Nurse leaders must have a fine
eye for separating the trivial but
apparently urgent many from the truly
important but rarely urgent few, and not
let their teams fall victim to the
80-20 rule. The bigger your goals,
the more focused you must be in
channeling your team's time
and resources.*

We live in an ADD world where there are endless demands for our attention, and where attention spans are becoming increasingly diminished. In his book *The Shallows: What the Internet is Doing to Our Brains*, Nicholas Carr documents how email, text messaging, web surfing, social media and other new technologies are causing physiological changes to the neural wiring of our brains, making it increasingly challenging for us to stay focused.

In one of the first self-help books of the modern era (*Wake Up and Live*, written during the Great Depression), author Dorothea Brande wrote that many people *choose to fail* to achieve what they say are their most important goals by becoming overcommitted to things that have nothing to do with achieving those goals. They fail at what really matters, she says, but they always have an excuse – they were too busy doing something else. If this was a problem in 1933, imagine how much more challenging it is today!

You will never *find* the time to do the things that are important but not urgent, like writing a book or pursuing advanced education (proof: have you ever *found* 15 minutes lying on the sidewalk?). You must *make* the time by being more focused in how you use your time. And as a leader, you can encourage your people to achieve their goals – to write their books and obtain their advanced degrees – by being more focused in how they use their time.

Target

The One Big Yes requires lots of little no's; the fewer targets you try to hit at one time, the more of them you will hit over a lifetime. If you want to change your corner of the world, you don't have time to waste watching reality TV or money to waste on shopping therapy.

The Pareto Principle (better known as the 80/20 rule) states that as a general principle, 20% of activity is responsible for 80% of results. In business, 20% of a company's customers will account for 80% of its revenue; in healthcare, 20% of patients account for 80% of healthcare costs. In your own work, it is likely that 20% of your effort is responsible for 80% of your substantive outcomes while the other 80% of your time is spent attending meetings and dealing with issues that do not directly contribute to achieving big goals.

If you can identify the 20% that's highly productive and do more of that, and do less of the other 80%, you will accomplish a great deal more. As Richard Koch wrote in his book *The 80/20 Principle*: "The trivial many comprise the prevalent inertia and ineffectiveness. The vital few are the breakthrough streaks of effectiveness, brilliance, and good fit. Most activity results in little value and little change. A few powerful interventions can have massive impact."

The way that you spend your time and money is a much better indicator of what your personal values really are than what you say those values are. Just say no to trivial distractions, diversions and temptations so that you can say yes to your One Big Yes.

Concentration

---

*Once you have identified your
key target goals, you must be willing
to concentrate your time, energy and
resources on the achievement
of those goals.*

Every human being has the same 24 hours in a day. One definition of genius is that it is the ability to intensively concentrate a healthy chunk of those 24 hours on one subject for an extended period. One of the tools that we use to help people concentrate on important goals is the DDQ (Direction Deflection Question – not Dairy Queen). Here are several examples:

- Will the way I am about to spend my next hour help me achieve an important goal (and if not, what would I do if that goal really was important to me)?

- Will what I am about to put in my mouth help me achieve my goal of attaining the ideal body weight (and if not, what would I be eating – or not eating)?

- Will this thing that I am about to spend my hard-earned cash on help me achieve my goal of being financially independent (and if not, can I live without it and save the money)?

At Midland Memorial Hospital we have seen people lose weight (in some cases a lot of weight), quit smoking, get out of debt, complete graduate degrees and other significant accomplishments as a result of participating in our "Proceed Until Apprehended" Culture of Ownership. When we ask what tools were most helpful to them, the DDQ is almost always one of the first things they mention.

Speed

In today's turbulent and fast-paced world, slow and steady does not always win the race. The rabbit population keeps exploding while tortoises are almost extinct.

Today's healthcare world is changing fast, and nurse leaders need to be quick and nimble to stay ahead of that curve. When you are moving fast toward a goal, you are less likely to be distracted by trivial matters or diverted down dead-end detours. For the nurse leader, "see one, do one, teach one" can also be a mantra for effective leadership because imbuing the team with a sense of urgency is paramount to hitting big targets like implementation of a new electronic health record or launching a community health program.

In his book *The Speed of Trust*, Stephen M.R. Covey wrote that the absence of trust in an organization is like a tax that makes everything slower and cost more. The nurse leader who fosters trust with transparency and openness fosters a workplace where that tax is minimized.

Because there are never enough hours in the day, and because no one has yet perfected the science of speed-sleeping, as a nurse leader it is incumbent upon you to make the best use of your waking hours by not allowing yourself or your team to become bogged down by trivia, drama, and toxic emotional negativity.

Momentum

---

*"Momentum is really a leader's
best friend. Sometimes it's the only
difference between winning and losing...
Momentum also makes a huge difference
in organizations. When you have no
momentum, even the simplest tasks can
seem to be insurmountable problems. But
when you have momentum on your side,
the future looks bright, obstacles appear
small, and trouble seems temporary."*

John C. Maxwell:
The 21 Irrefutable Laws of Leadership

Anyone who has ever gotten on and off the exercise roller coaster knows that it's a lot easier to stay in shape than it is to get back into shape once you've lost it. That is the power of momentum, and it applies in the organizational setting as well as the personal. Procrastination is the mortal enemy of momentum. Procrastination is pushing the work of today off into tomorrow with the result that you are perpetually living in the shadow of yesterday. It is the source of much personal misery and organizational failure.

At the organizational level, sustaining momentum is antidote to "program of the month" syndrome. When programs come and go without achieving a lasting impact it is rarely because the program was defective and much more likely that leadership did not make a priority of sustaining momentum. Overcoming resistance and procrastination – keeping the project on track after the initial flush of enthusiasm has worn off – is a marker of leadership character.

At Midland Memorial Hospital, the Daily Leadership Huddle, the Sacred 60 Leadership Rounds commitment to one hour per day rounding by every leader, and other formalized processes help to make sure that the leadership team does not backslide on its commitment to the Culture of Ownership. Routines and rituals like this are a great way to sustain momentum.

Chapter Ten

ENTHUSIASM

CORNERSTONES

Attitude

Energy

Curiosity

Humor

Enthusiasm is the master value. When you are enthusiastic
about your work and your life, it makes everything else easier.
And when you are not enthusiastic, it makes
everything else harder.

ENTHUSIASM

Without enthusiasm,
even play can seem a chore;
with enthusiasm,
even work can be fun.

Ralph Waldo Emerson wrote that nothing great was ever achieved without enthusiasm, and we could not agree more. Fortunately, whether you are enthusiastic is not determined by your genetic makeup – it is a choice that you make every hour of every day.

Working and living with enthusiasm makes it easier to work and live with each of the other values. It's easier to be authentic, to be courageous and persevering, to have a vision and be focused on its achievement when you are enthusiastic. And when you are not enthusiastic, it makes everything else all that much harder.

The nurse leader makes it her business to be enthusiastic, to set an example of it him or herself and to expect it from members of the team. Enthusiasm is a non-negotiable requirement for anyone in a leadership role. Nobody wants to follow a negative, grouchy, pessimistic manager who is clearly just in it for the paycheck.

Attitude

Attitude really is everything. Having a great attitude in and of itself will not make you a great nurse leader, but having a bad attitude will make you a bad nurse leader.

In our book *Building a Culture of Ownership in Healthcare* we referred to the prevalence of terms such as bullying, incivility, disrespect, burnout, and disengagement in the healthcare literature as "the healthcare crisis within." In her book *No Ego*, Cy Wakeman shares research suggesting that the average employee spends 2.5 hours per day on drama. Gallup research indicates that only one-in-four employees is fully engaged in the work. In administering the Values Coach Culture Assessment Survey we've seen results that suggest hospitals waste between five and twenty-five percent of their payroll budgets on people engaging such negative behaviors rather than doing the work they are being paid to do.

Southwest Airlines is famous for its "hire for attitude, train for school" hiring mantra (though especially for pilots they do screen carefully for skills!). Nurse leaders need to take that philosophy one step farther: hire for attitude, train for attitude, evaluate for attitude, and if necessary, terminate for attitude.

At Grinnell Regional Medical Center in Grinnell, Iowa, The Twelve Core Action Values is included in every employee's job description and accounts for fully 50 percent of every performance appraisal. As at Midland Health, GRMC's team of Certified Values Coach Trainers conducts the two-day course as part of new employee orientation so that every new associate knows what will be expected of them.

Energy

Energy is life. People with a lot of energy have a lot of life. If you are unhappy, chances are that the only thing standing between you and greater happiness is an expenditure of positive energy, both emotional and physical.

Effective nurse leaders know that they are just as responsible for the stewardship of human energy as they are for stewardship of the energy budget of their organization. They conscientiously stoke positive energy by incorporating stories, recognition, and rituals into their daily huddles. Beginning with their own example, they encourage people to be energy faucets who uplift their colleagues, and they have the courage to have what our friend Cheri Clancy calls "critical conversations" (in her book of that title) with the people who are energy drains.

Consider this: Two people are at an airport waiting for their flight. One person is doing pushups. The other is eating a double cheeseburger and reading the sports page. Which one of the two will have more energy to get some work done on the upcoming flight? And while bystanders will cluck at how strange it is to see someone doing pushups at an airport, deep down who do you think will earn their respect – the one doing pushups or the one eating the double cheeseburger and reading the sports page?

Human energy is the ultimate self-renewing resource – expending energy creates energy. In healthcare today, we need nurse leaders who are willing to stand out and do their pushups, at least metaphorically speaking.

Curiosity

---

*If you don't have a question, you
don't have a clue. If you aren't searching,
you are truly lost.*

McZen

The "insatiable curiosity" of the elephant's child in Rudyard Kipling's classic children's story earned him the distinctive long trunk that was the envy of his stub-nosed relatives, who all quickly followed his lead by running to the river to ask the crocodile to elongate their noses. It's a great metaphor for leadership. Leaders follow their curiosity into unknown territories. While the journey is sometimes painful, the outcome inspires others to follow.

Curiosity is closely related to caring. Nurse leaders with heart ask about the family members of team members because they care. They don't settle for superficial answers when looking into adverse patient events because they care. And whether it's asking about barcodes at the grocery store or how Disneyworld manages lines, even when not on the time clock they ask questions because they care.

In her book *Change Your Questions Change Your Life*, Marilee Adams wrote: "A world of questions is a world of possibility. Questions open our minds, connect us to each other, and shake outmoded paradigms." The way to get better answers is to ask better questions. That is the underlying principle of the 5-Whys total quality management technique. With each successive "Why?" the questions become more refined and the answers come closer to the truth of root cause.

Humor

In today's demanding and fast-changing healthcare environment, we need less Dr. Kildare and more Patch Adams. Humor can be the surest way to spark a spirit of enthusiasm in the face of stressful situations.

Laughter often really is the best medicine. Believing that to be the case, Dr. Madan Kataria, a physician in Mumbai, invited people to come together to practice what he came to call laughter yoga. Today, there are more than 60,000 laughter clubs in 60 different countries. People meet for a few minutes to laugh. There's no need for a standup comedian or a funny joke – someone just starts laughing. And because laughter is as contagious as flu bug in a kindergarten class, before long everyone is laughing hysterically. Check it out yourself – google "laughter clubs" and see if watching people laughing – laughing for no reason other than the sheer joy of a good laugh – doesn't start you doing it. And if that good belly laugh doesn't give you a shot of energy for the rest of your day.

Humor is most important when it is hardest to find – during times of greatest stress and adversity. The nurse leader with heart knows when to lighten things up with a smile, a laugh, or a funny story. As psychiatrist Edward Hallowell wrote in his book *Worry*, "Toxic worry almost always entails a loss of perspective; humor almost always restores it."

One caveat: Laughter is not really humor, and certainly not in the spirit of living values, if that laughter comes at someone's expense. Leave the put-down humor to television sitcoms – it has no place in a healing environment.

Chapter Eleven

SERVICE

CORNERSTONES

Helpfulness

Charity

Compassion

Renewal

I will earn the help I need in advance by helping other people now, and repay the help I receive by serving others later.

Thursday's Promise of The Self Empowerment Pledge

SERVICE

Service is not just what you do to help other people, it is also the attitude with which you do what you do. Help that is given with a surly, condescending, or judgmental spirit, or that is treated as a burdensome chore rather than as a professional privilege, is not really service.

Beginning with the pioneering work of Robert Greenleaf, there has been a growing recognition that the best type of leadership is servant leadership. That spirit is a prerequisite to be a nurse leader who leads from the heart. That leader fosters a culture of ownership where people see their job description as a floor and not as a ceiling; where the job duties for which they are accountable are just the platform upon which they add their own special touches, and where you never hear the words "not my job" as someone walks by a piece of paper on the floor or a patient crying in a wheelchair.

The greatest service nurse leaders can give is to help the people in their charge develop the capacity and the confidence to set big goals, to believe that they are capable of achieving those goals, and that they deserve to enjoy the fruits of their success. This also means protecting them from the baleful influence of the bullies and emotional vampires whose mission in life often appears to be living out that awful metaphor of nurses eating their young.

Whenever you reach out to help someone else, you often end up being the one who is helped most, as anyone who has ever volunteered at a soup kitchen or a Habitat for Humanity project, or participated in a mission trip, will attest. Remember: Whatever you most need in life, the best way for you to get it is to help someone else get it who needs it more than you do.

Helpfulness

The greatest part of your leadership legacy will not be created by what you have achieved yourself, but by the achievements of those you have helped along the way.

W ebster's Dictionary has two definitions for helpfulness: "1) the property of providing useful assistance; and 2) friendliness evidenced by a kindly and helpful disposition." Service is not just helping others, it is also the attitude with which you help them.

A commitment to helpfulness is especially important during challenging times of adversity. After Bonnie and Mark Barnes lost their son Patrick to a rare autoimmune disease, they established the DAISY Foundation to recognize extraordinary nurses. Today there are more than 2,800 DAISY hospitals around the world and nearly a million nurses have been nominated for DAISY Awards. Bonnie and Mark transformed what could have been a meaningless tragedy into the catalyst for a positive movement that is creating a lasting legacy. Appendix 5 describes the relationship between the DAISY Foundation and the American Organization of Nurse Executives.

We both love hiking on desert and mountain trails and have a special appreciation for the people who build cairns to mark those trails. The people who build these cairns are not doing for themselves – they already know where the trail goes and do not need cairns to guide them. They are building them for people they will in all likelihood never meet and doing it without any expectation of payment for their effort. That is a great metaphor for what servant leaders do.

Charity

True charity is not just giving of your money, it is also giving of your time and talents – giving what you can give and doing what you can do with a spirit of extravagant generosity.

Having a charitable heart means being kind, loving and compassionate towards others. This could be another colleague, the patient and family being cared for, or even a stranger on the street. A true spirit of charity is the lovely blending of gratitude for the many blessings of your life and compassion for those who are less fortunate. It is being generous with your money – but also being generous with smiles, hugs, and simple acts of kindness. A generous spirit encourages without judging or diminishing others.

We know from the stories of King Midas and Johnny Appleseed that a treasure hoarded is a treasure diminished while a treasure shared is a treasure multiplied. King Midas wanted everything that he touched to turn to gold to add to his hoard. His wish was granted, and he starved to death. Johnny Appleseed shared the wealth of his apple seeds across the land and fed future generations apples by the millions.

Midland Memorial Hospital was the first to take up The Pickle Challenge for Charity (see Appendix 3). As of this writing, more than 40 other hospitals and health systems have taken the challenge, raising more than $75,000 for charitable causes by turning more than a quarter of a million complaints into 25-cent contributions. That is putting your money where your heart is!

Compassion

*Compassion without action is
just a good intention.*

Merriam-Webster defines compassion as a "sympathetic consciousness of others' distress together with a desire to alleviate it." Nurses provide compassionate care regularly to relive the pain and suffering a patient or family member might have. We agree with what author Christina Dempsey wrote in her book *The Antidote to Suffering*: the physical suffering a patient experiences as a result of injuries or illnesses is inevitable, but emotional suffering caused by a lack of compassion on the part of caregivers should not be tolerated.

Dempsey describes compassionate connected care as the antidote to suffereing. The same principle applies to leading with heart, if for no other reason than everyone suffers at some point. Since we more often than not we are not aware of the individual's personal story, we should assume that as a leader we owe them compassionate connected care. And as a nurse leader, we owe it to our colleagues, patients and their families to provide compassionate connected care.

But we disagree with the Merriam-Webster definition above in one important respect: real compassion requires more than just a desire to help. Especially in healthcare, if it requires acting upon that desire.

Renewal

---

*You cannot pour from an empty pitcher.
Take time to renew yourself so that
you can continue to serve others with
attentiveness, caring and compassion.
And remember this – if you're not enjoying
the journey, the destination is likely
to be a disappointment.*

Nurses are, year after year, the most highly trusted professionals in the land. Unfortunately, they are also among the unhealthiest. Nurses tend to smoke more and be more overweight, to be more stressed out and sleep-deprived, to make less personal time for exercise and meditation, and in other ways to take care of themselves. This, as much as workload and other external stress factors, contributes to disengagement, burnout, and compassion fatigue.

Every nurse should make an ironclad commitment to practice the Nedlog Rule. Now, don't go running to your dictionary to look that word up because you won't find it there (at least not yet). Nedlog is the word Golden spelled backwards. The Nedlog Rule is the Golden Rule in reverse. Anything you would be willing to do for someone else if they asked you, you should be willing to ask the same for yourself when you need it. Including those things that restore your health and renew your spirit.

We recommend that you as a nurse leader have a special place in nature to which you can retreat to renew your spirits and refresh your energy, and that you make a commitment to spend time there – especially in those times when your soul is hurting.

Chapter Twelve

LEADERSHIP

CORNERSTONES

Expectations

Example

Encouragement

Celebration

Management is a job description, leadership is a life decision. Anyone who takes to heart and acts upon Core Action Values 1-through-11 will, through their example and the expectations they set for themselves and others, both influence and inspire the people around them. That is the best definition we know of what a nurse leader with heart does – influences and inspires others.

LEADERSHIP

"There is a 100 percent chance that you can be a role model for leadership. There is a 100 percent chance that you can influence someone else's performance. There is a 100 percent chance that you can affect what someone else thinks, says, and does. There is a 100 percent chance that you will make a difference in other people's lives."

James M. Kouzes and Barry Z. Posner:
A Leader's Legacy

Leadership authority Joel Barker says that a leader is someone who takes you to a place to which you did not know you wanted to go. That entails both creating a vision of that place and inspiring people to undertake the journey. We add that a leader is someone who takes you to that place by helping you become the person that you did not know you could be. That likewise entails helping the individual see their own potential and inspiring them to pursue authentic goals and grow into the people they are meant to be.

Leadership becomes a value when it is more than just what you do for a living but rather becomes a personal philosophy, a perspective on looking at challenges and opportunities, and a commitment to serving others through your example and the expectations that you set. We agree with what author James Autry wrote in his book *Love and Profit*: leadership is largely a matter of love and caring, of creating a community of people who encourage each other and work towards common goals.

You can be a manager by holding people accountable for achieving results, but you can only be a leader by helping people take ownership for their results. It takes brains to be a manager – to be a leader you must also have heart.

Expectations

Leaders create high expectations for themselves and for the members of their teams, then seek to encourage and enforce those expectations with cultural norms rather than through hierarchical accountability.

In his book *Weird Ideas that Work*, Stanford professor Robert Sutton wrote that more than 500 studies on the power of the self-fulfilling prophecy "find that, independent of other factors, when leaders believe their subordinates will perform well, positive expectations lead to better performance. And the converse holds for [low expectations and] poor performance." The nurse leader with heart takes a tough love approach to having high expectations that people will bring positive attitudes to work, will support and never undermine coworkers, and will represent their organization with pride, both on and off the job.

But she also recognizes that trying to enforce those expectations with hierarchical accountability – the carrot and stick approach – will eventually become counterproductive, and thus seeks to establish cultural norms to enforce these expectations through positive peer pressure. Think of this: When was the last time you had to discipline a coworker for lighting a cigarette while at work? It almost certainly will have been taken care of long before your intervention was required. Imagine a workplace that had the same cultural norms against the spiritual pollution of toxic emotional negativity that now prevail against the physical pollution of cigarette smoke.

One more thing: If you want to achieve success beyond your wildest expectations, you must begin with wild expectations.

Example

"A king does not abide within his tent
while his men bleed and die upon the
field. A king does not dine while his men
go hungry, nor sleep when they stand at
watch upon the wall. A king does not
command his men's loyalty through fear
nor purchase it with gold; he earns their
love by the sweat of his own back and the
pains he endures for their sake.
That which comprises the harshest burden,
a king lifts first and sets down last.
A king does not require service of those
he leads but provides it to them.
He serves them, not they him."

Steven Pressfield: Gates of Fire

Anyone who presumes to be a nurse leader must give up many freedoms. As a nurse leader, you give up the freedom to join in on meetings of the alternative BMW Club (Bellyaching, Moaning, Whining and Complaining). You give up the freedom to participate in gossip and rumor-mongering, even as a passive participant, because such disrespectful behavior violates the dignity of the person being gossiped about and the integrity of the organization. You give up the freedom to in any way act in ways that are counter to the values of your organization because you are being paid to be an example of those values.

It's been said that there are only three types of leadership: example, example and example. People will watch what you do and the attitude with which you do it far more acutely than they will listen to what you say. And their performance will rarely if ever exceed the example that you set through your own performance. And in following your example they will, for better or worse, be setting an example for others.

By leading with heart, the nurse leader nurtures the hearts of those for whom she is responsible.

Encouragement

Transforming leadership is ultimately spiritual leadership. It is encouraging people to be their best selves and to do their best work, not because they fear being held accountable but because they want to live their values. It is connecting them to the higher purpose and greater meaning of their everyday work.

James O'Toole's book *Leadership A-to-Z* is structured as a dictionary, and under the letter C he asks why so many leaders fail to appreciate that an essential element of leading is Cheerleading. We wonder why, given the importance of storytelling for shaping culture, more leaders do not practice the skills to become better storytellers.

Try this. Google "What Teachers Make" and watch teacher/poet Taylor Mali *perform* his poem at a poetry slam. Then google "What Teachers Make TED talk" and watch a younger and less-experienced Taylor Mali *recite* his poem at a TED conference. Then google "What Teachers Make text" and just *read* the words. Now ask yourself which of those three approaches – performing, reciting or reading – will have the most powerful impact on the audience. Which would be most likely to encourage a college student to consider teaching as a career, or to encourage a teacher to take greater pride in his work – a performance, a recitation, or being asked to read the poem. Which approach would make you a better nurse leader?

Every great leader knows that words alone do little to inspire followers. The best form of encouragement truly is cheerleading – letting your passion shine through as you encourage others to do their work and live their lives with passion.

Celebration

The best leaders foster teamwork, creativity, community and a spirit of fellowship by celebrating personal and group achievements. They also celebrate good faith failures, turning those experiences into the platform for future success and achievement.

According to the Gallup Organization, one of the most important determinants of whether employees are fully engaged in their work is if they have good friends on the job. Effective leaders go out of their way to cultivate an empowering culture and a positive workplace environment. The best leaders take the time to recognize and celebrate both successes and good faith failures.

It is especially important to find ways to celebrate good faith failures. If people are afraid of being punished for failure, you will eventually lose your most creative and talented people. On the other hand, when you have a reputation for standing behind the people even if they have failed spectacularly, you will attract more creative and daring people, and keep the ones you have. This is an essential tenet of the just culture philosophy.

One more thing: Rituals have always been an important way for humans to bring a sense of structure and purpose to their work, yet in today's workplace we're too busy for rituals (we've replaced them with meetings). What can you do to restore the spirit and practice of rituals in your organization?

CONCLUSION

*A leader is someone who influences
others to expect more of themselves and inspires them to do the
work necessary to achieve their most important goals and to
become the best people they are capable of being.*

Management is a job description; leadership is a life decision. The nurse leader with heart inspires others to
become leaders themselves who live the four essential charac-
teristics of values-based leadership: Character, Expectations,
Fellowship, and Quest.

Character: Values-based leadership begins with self-lead-
ership. The Greek philosopher Heraclitus said that character
is destiny. Building character is a lifelong, day-after-day commitment to doing the right thing – even when it is difficult
or frightening. Knowing your values, and making a commitment to living those values, is the non-negotiable prerequisite
to being a leader with heart, a leader who leaves a lasting legacy.

Expectations: The best leaders expect greatness – from
themselves and from those they lead. They strive to see more
in others than others see in themselves, and to help them

become the person they never thought they could be. At a personal level, these expectations are reflected in the way their colleagues raise their sites regarding their own education and accomplishments. At the organizational level these expectations are reflected in higher performance standards for clinical quality and patient experience, productivity and financial performance, and other key indicators of an organization that is on the journey from good to great.

Fellowship: According to the Gallup organization, one of the best predictors of a highly engaged workforce is that people have best friends at work. The nurse leader with heart strives to create a workplace culture characterized by respect and camaraderie, mutual support and encouragement, joy and passion, and that is intolerant of the sorts of toxic emotional negativity that inevitably poison such a culture. A workplace where people laugh often and occasionally cry together.

Quest: Healthcare should be a calling, not just a job. The nurse leader with heart inspires people to see human beings with hearts and souls, to commit themselves to heal when they can and to care always. A Culture of Ownership requires all hands on deck, all animated by the spirit of a noble quest.

We love the beautiful cover that Lisa Peterson at Studio 6 Sense created for this book because it captures the two essential qualities of values-base leadership: the technical dimension is reflected in the stethoscope around the neck and the spiritual dimension is reflected in the heart worn on the pocket.

APPENDIX

THE TWELVE CORE ACTION VALUES

---

*"The Twelve Core Action Values is like graduate
school for the seven habits."*

*David G. Altman, Chief Operating Officer
Center for Creative Leadership*

M ost people intuitively have good solid values, and none more so than those who choose the healing professions for a career. But very few of us have seriously thought about what our own personal values are, much less how those values can be better reflected in our calendars and checkbook registers, in how we make decisions and deal with conflict, and in the goals and dreams by which we define our futures.

The Twelve Core Action Values, and the 48 cornerstones that put action into those values, are universal values that transcend any particular religious belief or non-belief, political opinions, ethnic background or any other factor. From Authenticity (Core Action Value #1) to Leadership (Core Action Value #12), these are the values that you aspire to live and that you want the people of your team to aspire to live.

As of this writing in early 2018, Values Coach has prepared 675 Certified Values Coach Trainers (CVCT) in 58 different healthcare organizations to share the course with their coworkers. Those CVCTs, in turn, have taught or team-taught the course for more than 12,000 of their colleagues at work. In many cases, people take what they have learned home with them. For some participants the course has been a life-changing experience.

Lori Forbus, RN, Certified Values Coach Trainer in the Midland Memorial Hospital Culture of Ownership Classroom

THE SELF
EMPOWERMENT PLEDGE

"Empowerment is not something that can be given, it must be claimed. No one can empower you but you, and only you have given yourself that power, no one can take it away from you."

Joe Tye: *The Florence Prescription:*
From Accountability to Ownership

The Self Empowerment Pledge includes seven promises one for each day of the week, promises that you make to yourself. We challenge people to make each day's promise at least four times per day – out loud when they can and in a group whenever possible. The more often you make the promises, the more painful it is to catch yourself breaking them. That pain creates cognitive dissonance and the person motivation to make the attitude and behavior changes necessary to begin keeping the promises. And as those things change, you begin to achieve better outcomes.

We have seen people lose weight and get in better shape, get out of debit, complete graduate degrees and finally write books they had always dreamed of writing, quite smoking, and generally improve their lives by committing to these promises. In the story "Promises" one of the chapters in the book *Chicken Soup for the Soul: Inspiration for Nurses* by Amy Newmark and LeAnn Thieman Bob Dent tells the story of an RN at Midland Memorial Hospital who used these seven promises to help him break a tenacious drug addiction.

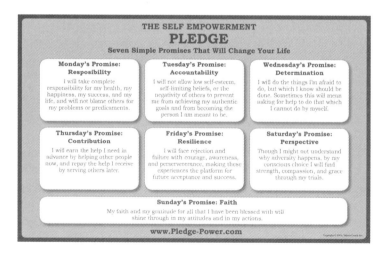

THE SELF EMPOWERMENT
PLEDGE
Seven Simple Promises That Will Change Your Life

Monday's Promise: Resposibility

I will take complete responsibility for my health, my happiness, my success, and my life, and will not blame others for my problems or predicaments.

Tuesday's Promise: Accountability

I will not allow low self-esteem, self-limiting beliefs, or the negativity of others to prevent me from achieving my authentic goals and from becoming the person I am meant to be.

Wednesday's Promise: Determination

I will do the things I'm afraid to do, but which I know should be done. Sometimes this will mean asking for help to do that which I cannot do by myself.

Thursday's Promise: Contribution

I will earn the help I need in advance by helping other people now, and repay the help I receive by serving others later.

Friday's Promise: Resilience

I will face rejection and failure with courage, awareness, and perserverance, making these experiences the platform for future acceptance and success.

Saturday's Promise: Perspective

Though I might not understand why adversity happens, by my conscious choice I will find strength, compassion, and grace through my trials.

Sunday's Promise: Faith

My faith and my gratitude for all that I have been blessed with will shine through in my attitudes and in my actions.

www.Pledge-Power.com

THE PICKLE PLEDGE

"Because of our commitment to The Pickle Pledge we are happier, healthier, more productive, and better off in virtually every dimension of our lives. If you make the commitment, you will be too."

Joe Tye and Bob Dent: Pickle Pledge:
Creating a More Positive Healthcare Culture –
One Attitude at a time

The Pickle Pledge is a simple (though not always easy) promise to turn every compliant into a blessing (gratitude) or a constructive suggestion (initiative). It is a powerful antidote to toxic emotional negativity – as reflected in chronic complaining and gossiping, bullying and disrespectful behavior, disengagement and burnout, and other emotional barriers to a positive workplace culture.

The Pickle Challenge for Charity is a one-week period during which people challenge themselves and each other to turn every complaint into a 25-cent contribution to a charity selected by the organization. As of this writing in early 2018, 43 different healthcare organizations have raised more than $75,000 for charitable causes by turning more than a quarter-million complaints into donations. More important, these organizations have made people more aware of how much work and life be. Just as the non-negotiable first step to creating a healthier workplace was to prohibit cigarette smoking, so too the first step to building a more positive culture of ownership is replacing toxic emotional negativity with a spirit of gratitude and initiative.

I've Taken The Pickle Pledge

"I will turn every complaint into either a blessing or constructive suggestion."

By taking **The Pickle Pledge**, I am promising myself that I will no longer waste my time and energy on blaming, complaining, and gossiping, nor will I commiserate with those who steal my energy with their blaming, complaining, and gossiping.

* So-called because chronic complainers look like they were born with a dill pickle stuck in their mouths.

VALUESCOACH.COM • THEFLORENCECHALLENGE.COM

TRI-COUNCIL FOR NURSING, NURSING CIVILITY PROCLAMATION

WHEREAS, the public views nurses as the most ethical and honest profession in the United States.

WHEREAS, overt and covert acts of incivility, disrespect, bullying, and other toxic emotional behaviors have a negative effect on nurses and others including burnout, fatigue, depression, panic attacks, substance abuse, moral distress, among other physiological effects.

WHEREAS, toxic emotional behaviors have a negative effect on organizations including employee engagement and patient satisfaction, clinical quality and patient safety, nursing turnover, and can exacerbate the nursing shortage.

WHEREAS, toxic emotional behaviors contribute to poor communication and teamwork, a leading cause in preventable harm in those who entrust their lives to nurses and other healthcare professionals to care for them.

WHEREAS, nurses are ethically obligated to care for each other and those we provide care to with civility regardless of race, ethnicity, socio-economic status, gender, physical ability, religious affiliation, language, sexual orientation, age, political orientation, veteran status, occupational status, geographical location and any other cultural diversities.

NOW, THEREFORE, be it resolved that we, the Tri-Council for Nursing, do hereby proclaim that Nursing Civility is to be practiced throughout the United States of America to establish healthy work environments that embraces and values cultural diversity, inclusivity, and equity.

We, the Tri-Council for Nursing call upon all nurses to recognize Nursing Civility and take steps to systematically reduce all acts of incivility in their professional practice, workplace environments, and in our communities

American Association of Colleges of Nursing (AACN)

American Nurses Association (ANA)

American Organization of Nurse Executives (AONE)

National League for Nursing (NLN)

AONE AND THE DAISY FOUNDATION

- Founded November, 1999 by members of Patrick Barnes's family in memory of the extraordinary, compassionate care provided to Patrick by his nurses.

- In January, 2008 AONE became DAISY's first Supportive Association. At the time, there were 182 hospitals honoring their nurses with The DAISY Award. DAISY had its first display at a nursing conference at AONE's Annual Meeting in Seattle. We have been at every annual meeting since then.

- At AONE's Annual Meeting in 2015, The DAISY Nurse Leader Award was introduced at a breakfast gathering. In 2016 at a Sunrise Session, Drs. Lesly Kelly and Cindy Lefton presented top-line findings of their study of the impact of The DAISY Award on compassion fatigue and compassion satisfaction.

- Today...
  - » There are over 3,000 healthcare facilities and schools of nursing committed to honoring their nurses, nurse leaders, nurse-led teams, nursing faculty and students with DAISY's recognition programs.

  - » DAISY is international, recognizing nurses in all 50 states and 17 other countries.

  - » Over 1 million DAISY nominations have been written by patients, families, and colleagues.

  - » Over 100,000 nurses have been honored.

  - » Research, conducted by the Foundation and others, now underscores the impact of The DAISY Award on a healthy work environment, nurse engagement and the patient/family experience.

  - » 28 professional nursing organizations are DAISY Supportive Associations. AONE was the first and is the only one to be featured on our banners and other materials.

BOB DENT'S LEADERSHIP PHILOSOPHY

I believe leadership carries the responsibility of being a positive example in the workplace. To accomplish this, it is important for me to be accessible, approachable and highly visible with our people leading at every interaction. I schedule time each day to complete **Leadership Rounds** to our people and patients.

I believe leaders have the responsibility to **Inspire a Shared Vision** recognizing the current state and our future related to the mission, vision, core values and the strategic priorities of our hospital.

I believe in **Professional Governance** where staff are empowered to challenge our current policies, procedures and practices making decisions important to improve the workplace environment and the patient's experience of care. None of us is as smart as all of us.

I believe in **Our People First**. I have the responsibility to reward, recognize, and celebrate the contributions of individuals and teams. I believe our people will be and perform at their best with the tools they have. As leaders, we have to assure our people are well cared for and have the tools they need. People work for people, not organizations.

I believe in **Safety Above All** with our patients, visitors and each other. To accomplish this, it is important that I am approachable. People need to feel comfortable and safe reporting unsafe practices.

I believe in **Our Mission Always**. I use our mission to guide the actions and decision-making of our teams.

I believe in a **Culture of Ownership**. In the spirit of proceed until apprehended, I encourage people to be creative and innovative exceeding the basis of their roles and responsibilities. I do not tolerate a lack of ownership, indecision, or not being prepared.

I believe in **Lifelong Learning**. I take complete responsibility for my own growth and development by staying involved in professional organizations, maintaining appropriate certifications, and reading pertinent material staying ahead of impending changes to the healthcare environment.

I believe **Communication is Key!** I believe in open, honest, and ethical communication, and being completely transparent. I will be upfront, above board, and direct with courtesy, professionalism, and mutual respect. I do not tolerate open hostility, anger and a failure to treat people with courtesy and respect.

I believe in **Excellence**. I have the responsibility of working with our teams to establish SMART goals for measuring progress (not perfection) towards our key performance indicators. I believe results are very important.

I believe in **Interprofessional Collaboration**. I have the responsibility to assure we have adequate representation in an environment of inclusivity to accomplish our shared vision and goals.

I believe the most important role of a leader is to build **Trusting Relationships**. A leader's circle of influence is more important than authority or control. Leadership is about discipline and intelligence, not about who has the heavier hand.

Bob Dent,
DNP, MBA, RN, NEA-BC, CENP, FACHE, FAAN
SVP, Chief Operating and Chief Nursing Officer
Midland Memorial Hospital

BECAUSE YOU NEED A CULTURAL BLUEPRINT FOR THE INVISIBLE ARCHITECTURE™ OF YOUR ORGANIZATION

When it comes to creating both a great employee experience and a great patient experience, the Invisible Architecture of core values, organization culture, and workplace attitude have a bigger impact than the visible architecture of bricks and mortar.

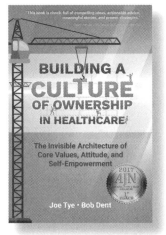

In this award-winning book, Joe Tye and Bob Dent share a proven process for creating a Cultural Blueprint to build a more positive Culture of Ownership that enhances employee commitment, service quality, customer satisfaction, productivity, and your ability to recruit and retain the best people.

Available at Amazon.com or NursingKnowledge.org

VALUES COACH INC.
www.ValuesCoach.com
319-624-3889

BECAUSE CULTURE DOESN'T CHANGE UNLESS PEOPLE CHANGE

– and People won't change Unless They Are Given New Tools and Inspired to Use Them

Joe Tye is a nationally-recognized speaker on cultural transformation and personal empowerment. He is the author or coauthor of 15 books and dozens of journal articles on personal and business success and speaks for hospital, corporate and association events across the county.

Joe will share unique strategies to help your people to be more positive and self-empowered and inspire them to be part of a Culture of Ownership in your organization.

"You did an outstanding job in your presentation. It was perfect for our culture journey in our organization. Feedback has been excellent. Actually the best we ever had since we started these system wide manager meeting a few years back. This large group meets twice per year so the day needs to be impactful. You were very impactful."

Joe Devine, President & CEO of Kennedy Health

VALUES COACH INC.

www.ValuesCoach.com

319-624-3889

BECAUSE NO ONE EVER CHECKS THE OIL IN A RENTAL CAR

With more than 500,000 copies in print, *The Florence Prescription* is helping hospitals and health systems everywhere move from a culture of accountability to a culture of ownership.

At just **$5** per book, this is the much appreciated gift to your people that is also a great investment in your organization.

The Third Edition features important new content including a new foreword by AHA Chair Nancy Howell Agee and a new introduction by AONE President Bob Dent.

Order at:
TheFlorenceChallenge.com
or by calling 319-624-3889

"The Florence Prescription is a work of art!"

Molly Seals, System Vice President, Human Resources Program Mercy Health, Youngstown, OH

VALUES COACH INC.

www.ValuesCoach.com
319-624-3889